I Was Never in Her Tummy

Luke's Adoption Story

Written by Sally Erickson
Illustrated by Ali Holley

ISBN: 978-0-578-92328-4

To Luke, of course.
Love, Mom

My name is **Luke**

and I have a story to tell.

Now listen closely

so I don't have to yell.

My mom's name is **Sally.**

And she's just the best!

But the story of how we became a family

ain't like all the rest.

My mom didn't give birth to me.

I was NEVER in her tummy!

But she's my MOM, I tell you.

After all...I'm no dummy.

"So how did she become your mom?" you may ask.

Well, it's quite the story.

Mom says it's a miracle and God gets the glory.

I'm ADOPTED.

That's kind of a weird word,
I know.

It means I have lots of people who love me though.

ADOPT:
TO CHOOSE TO HAVE ONE JOIN YOUR FAMILY FOREVER

My birth mom is named *Sarah.*

She has red hair...just like me.

She lives far away now,

but she's as sweet as can be.

My birth dad is named *Kevin*.

His eyes are bright blue.

Mom says I have his eyes

because mine sparkle too.

Kevin and Sarah weren't married when I was born and they didn't have much money. They weren't sure what to do. It really wasn't funny.

They knew they couldn't provide all of the things I would need. Because kids need lots of food and clothes. And toys, indeed!

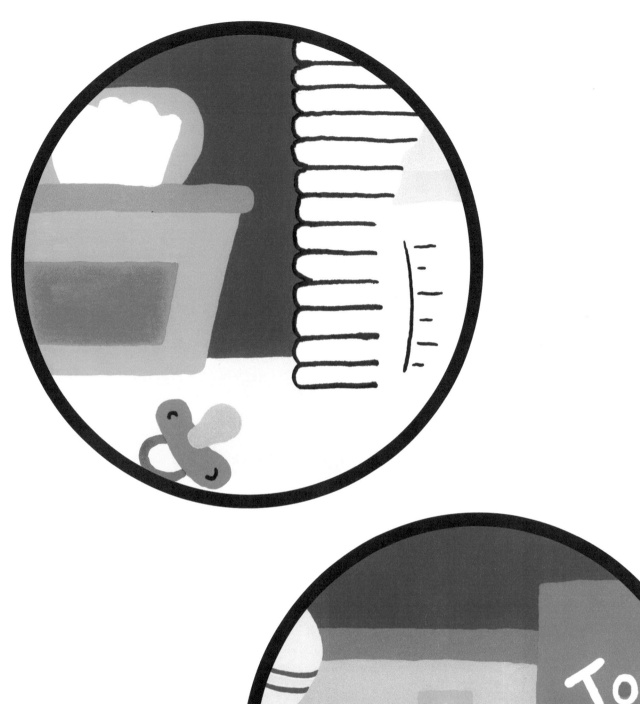

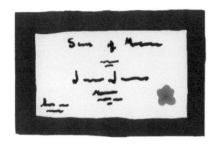

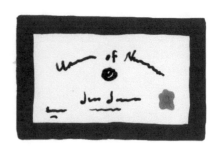

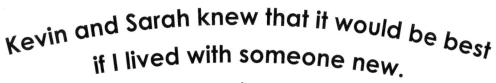

Kevin and Sarah knew that it would be best
if I lived with someone new.
But just not anybody would do...
They worked with Julie.
A social worker is she.
She knew lots of people who wanted a baby.
A sweet baby like me!

Julie showed them photo books with pictures of lots of families.

Families of all sorts.

Some that read books.

And some that played sports.

Some built sailboats
and lived near the sea.

Some planted
gardens
and drank sweet
tea.

Some climbed high mountains...
mountains in Peru.

But some stayed home
and made chicken
cordon bleu.

Some had
lots
of kids.

**And some
had
none.**

But a special family
caught
Kevin and Sarah's
attention.

**A
family
of
one.**

A tall woman, with curly blond hair.
Her name is Sally.
**She wanted to be a mom
more than any poll
could tally.**

Sally is a writer.

She works with words all day long.

She writes stories about families and how God makes them strong.

So Kevin and Sarah met with Sally,
and they knew right away.

They wanted her to be my **mommy**,
so I went home with her to stay.

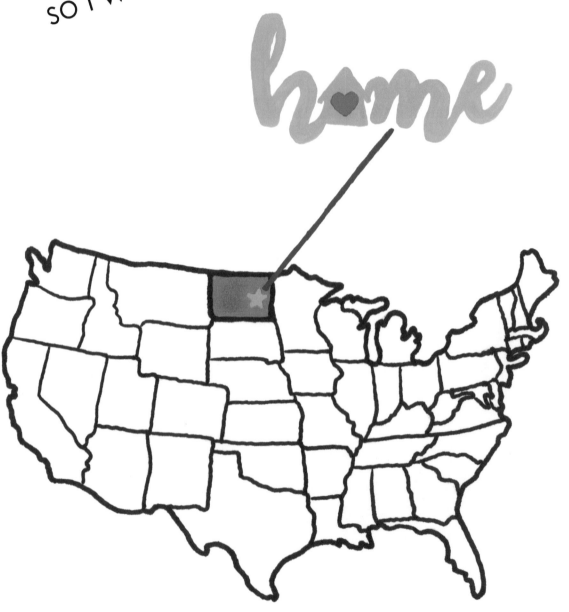

Sally had never been a mom before
but quickly she did learn.

She changed some pretty stinky diapers
and my love she did earn.

My mom and I are a pretty special family.

We're like two peas in a pod.

Adoption is a true miracle specifically designed by God.

Our family includes Grandpa & Grandma.

And my Auntie Kate.

She has red hair, too!

It's pretty great.

Kevin and Sarah are
always in our
hearts.

**We think about
them
every day.**

They're a part of
our
family too.

**We ask God to
watch over them
every night
when we pray.**

Love is the glue that binds

our family together.

It's pretty sticky glue.

We'll be a family

forever!

This is most

certainly

TRUE.

Some families look different, and that's OK. My family is just right for me. Love and faith are the roots of our family tree.

Well, that's what I wanted
to tell you about today.

That's my
adoption story.

It really is a
miracle
and God
gets the
glory.

CPSIA information can be obtained
at www.ICGtesting.com
Printed in the USA
LVHW072212160721
692933LV00001B/27